Australian
NURSERY RHYMES

Written by Colin Thiele

Illustrated by Wendy DePaauw

hinkler

Published by Hinkler Books Pty Ltd
45–55 Fairchild Street
Heatherton Victoria 3202 Australia
www.hinkler.com.au

First published by Weldon Kids Pty Ltd 1992

Illustration and design © Weldon Kids Pty Ltd
Text © Colin Thiele
Cover design © Hinkler Books Pty Ltd 2010

Project coordinator: Leah Walsh
Cover design: Ruth Comey
Prepress: Graphic Print Group

ISBN: 978 1 7418 5290 5

Printed and bound in China

Australian
NURSERY RHYMES

Written by Colin Thiele

Illustrated by Wendy DePaauw

hinkler

Sing a song of bellbirds, a forest full of sound,
Little notes of silver tinkling to the ground,
When the new day opens the bells begin to ring,
Isn't that a lovely way to wake each living thing?

Wombat is a pudding, a pudding firm and plump,
A snuffling sort of pudding with a rather rounded rump,
He rambles and he burrows in the dirt beside the track
With his stumpy legs plod-plodding, and the moonlight on his back.

Bowerbird, Bowerbird,
What have you there?
A place for display
That is lovely and rare.
Bowerbird, Bowerbird,
Of what is it made?
Of white bones and seashells
And coral and jade.

Frill-necked Lizard
Lay on his gizzard,
Relaxed in the shade of a rock,
But he raised up his frill
At a tourist from Nhill
Who promptly collapsed from the shock.

*I*n a hidden anthill,

With his sticky tongue,

Echidna picks off termites

Faster than a gun.

But as soon as danger threatens

His spines stand thick and tight;

If you sit down on Echidna

You'll get the point all right.

When wetlands shine
Like panes of glass
The Magpie Geese
Come teeming past.
Where lotus blooms
And reeds renew
They seek lagoons
in Kakadu.

Black Snake flows by like liquid glass
Through tussocks, leaves, and tufts of grass,
His belly red like coals aglow —
Stand back, stand back, and let him go.

What a magic moment,
What a marvellous sight,
From the towering cliffs of
The Great Australian Bight;
Whales in the ocean,
With babies at their side,
Cavorting where the combers
Rise and arch and slide.

When monsoon storms and flooding rains
Resound across the tropic North,
The armour-plated Crocodile
Stirs himself and lumbers forth,
But though he comes with wink and smile
Beware, beware, the Crocodile.

Wallaby, Wallaby,
Tidy and neat,
Flaunting your tail
And fine yellow feet;
High in the mountains —
Your place of renown —
You are tougher than whipcord
But as gentle as down.

Sea Lion and Dugong met one day
Beyond the blue edge of the bay,
When Shark came cruising idly by.
Said Sea Lion, looking rather shy,
`I think, my friend, that it would pay
To turn and swim the other way'.

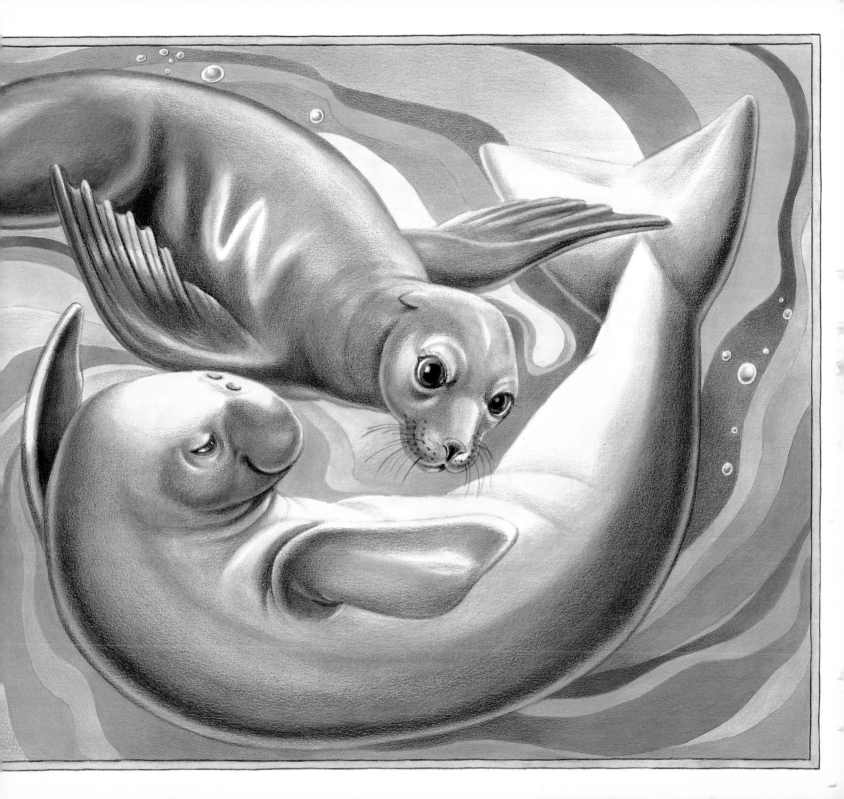

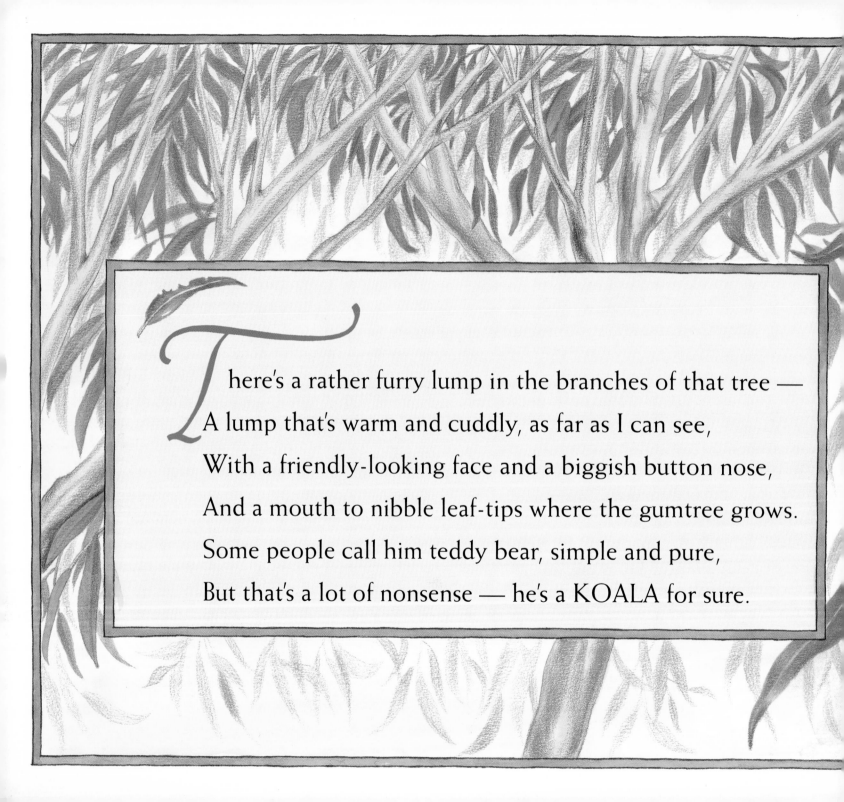

There's a rather furry lump in the branches of that tree —

A lump that's warm and cuddly, as far as I can see,

With a friendly-looking face and a biggish button nose,

And a mouth to nibble leaf-tips where the gumtree grows.

Some people call him teddy bear, simple and pure,

But that's a lot of nonsense — he's a KOALA for sure.

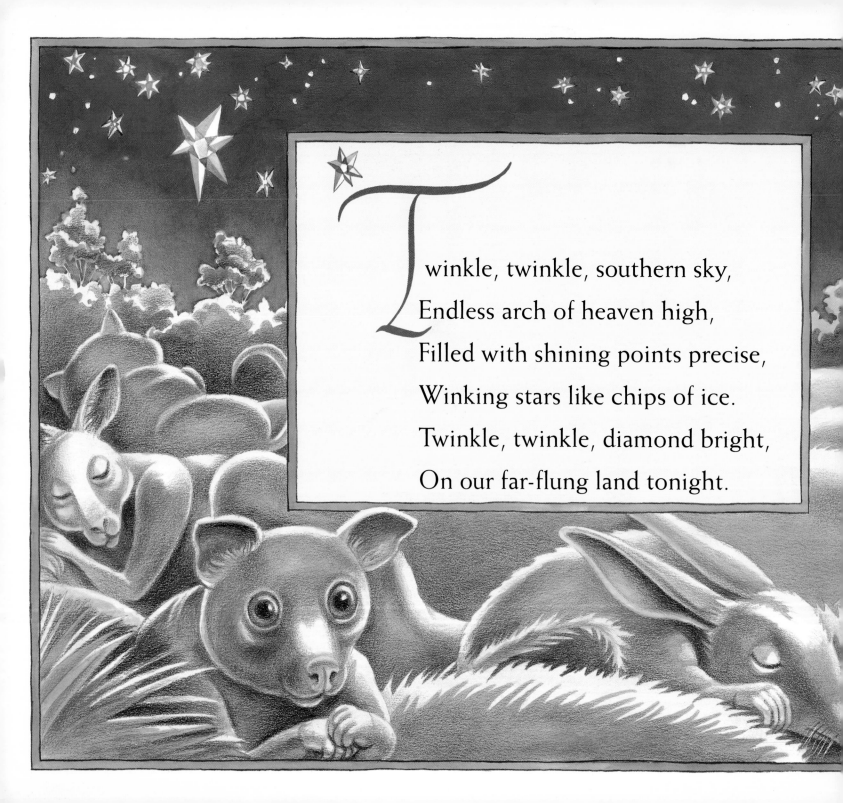

Twinkle, twinkle, southern sky,
Endless arch of heaven high,
Filled with shining points precise,
Winking stars like chips of ice.
Twinkle, twinkle, diamond bright,
On our far-flung land tonight.

BELLBIRDS

The bellbird got its name from its call, which sounds like a tinkling bell. Its nest is shaped like a cup and the bellbird likes to put caterpillars - often hairy ones! - around the top of the nest.

WOMBATS

Wombats live in burrows which have many entrances and below the ground all these burrows divide and connect, having many different 'rooms'. Wombats are nocturnal, and are herbivores (which means they feed only on parts of plants such as leaves and roots and don't eat meat).

SATIN BOWERBIRDS

In the shadows of the forest the male bird looks black, but in the sunshine it is deep shiny-blue. The male builds the bower out of sticks and decorates it with shells, flowers and any blue objects it can find.

FRILL-NECKED LIZARDS

These wonderful lizards can grow to 85 cm long. The lizard gets its name from the frill of skin around its neck and when it gets upset or angry it opens its mouth up wide and makes the frill stand up, something like an umbrella.

ECHIDNAS

In Australia, echidnas live in all sorts of different places - cold, snowy mountains, wet rainforests, and even hot and very dry deserts. The echidna is also called a spiny anteater and it uses its long, sticky tongue to lick out the ants and termites from their nests. If scared, they will curl up into a tight ball of spikes or dig themselves into the ground.

MAGPIE GEESE

The magpie goose once lived all over Australia but it is now found only in northern Australian swamps and grasslands where it feeds on water plants.

RED-BELLIED BLACK SNAKES

This snake is very shy and moves away quickly if it is disturbed, but it is also poisonous and you should stay well away if you see one.

WHALES

Every time a whale takes a breath, small amounts of water go down its throat. To make sure this water doesn't go into the whale's lungs, it is trapped in a special chamber. When a whale blows water through its spout it is getting rid of this water.

CROCODILES

There are only two types of crocodile in Australia, the freshwater crocodile and the estuarine crocodile. The estuarine crocodile lives in salt water (especially where the river meets the sea) and will attack people careless enough to swim in their waterways, but the freshwater crocodile prefers to stay away from people. However, to be on the safe side, stay well away from all crocodiles!

WALLABIES

Wallabies and kangaroos belong to the same family but wallabies are usually much smaller. Amoung the types of wallabies are brush wallabies, rock wallabies, and scrub wallabies (often called pademelons).

KOALAS

Koalas are found only in the Australian states of Victoria, New South Wales, Queensland and now South Australia. They spend their days in the trees sleeping and eating the leaves of their favourite tree, the eucalypt.

SEA LIONS

The Australian sea lion is the world's rarest sea lion and it is believed that there are only between 3,000 and 5,000 left.

DUGONGS

The dugong looks part seal and part whale. It is sometimes called a sea-cow because it spends much of its time grazing on seagrass in shallow water.